The Bow Af   in

story by Kimberly Martyn DeMeo

Rosie Ann came home
from school one day
in early spring.

Teachers whispered,
parents talked
of changes things would bring.

There was a
scary virus,
that kept us all
contained.

So little Rosie Ann
looked out to find
the bow after the rain.

Her school books,
they stayed in her house,
her backpack on the floor.

Her friends could not
come there to play.

What was normal
was no more.

The nightly news
was on TV
And people
passed the blame.

So little Rosie Ann
looked out to find
the bow after the rain.

One day when mom was looking sad, Rosie Ann called out her name.

"Don't worry," she said with a smile. "Look for the bow after the rain."

"What's that? What's it mean?" asked her mom. She sounded quite amused.

"When things are scary," Rosie Ann said, "those are the words I use."

When storms roll in, dark and
cold and thunder rumbles
clouds,

The wind will whoosh them
far away and the colors
will come out.

The sun peeks out to warm
you, lets you know you'll be
okay.

And the magic gift
you're given is the
bow after the rain.

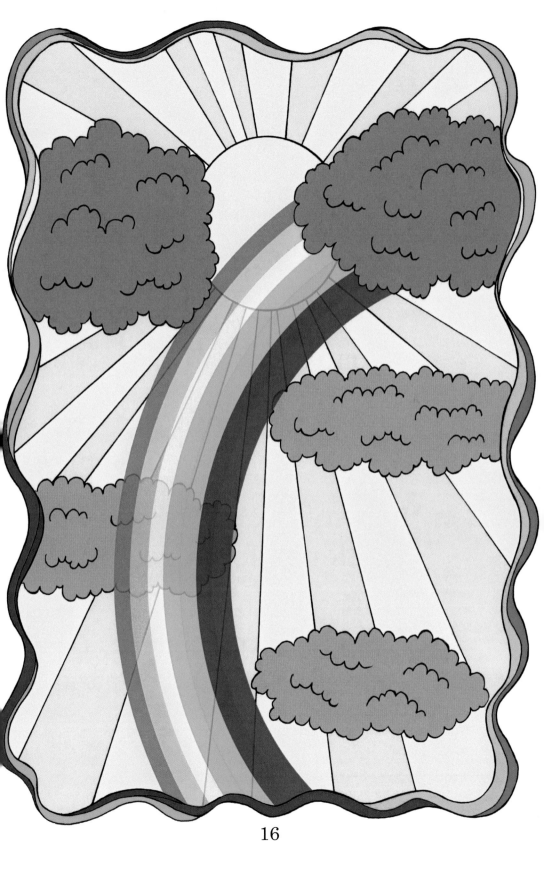

We go to school on
Zoom now.

Wearing PJ's all day
is a thing!

Work from home is a
challenge for sure,
but with breaks
to walk, stretch and sing!

There is cooking
in the kitchen,
movies streaming
on TV.

Decorations cover
all the walls,
giving hope for all to see.

We eat dinner together as
a family, we fill tables with
puzzles and games.

We have drive-by birthday
parties and those memories
will remain.

Fishing, bike rides, sidewalk
chalk, catching bugs or frogs
or bubbles, running through
sprinklers or eating ice cream
—
these things help people
forget their troubles.

Six feet of safety
is what we do now.

We wear masks
to keep out bad germs.

Two weeks inside
if we are exposed

These are
"new normal" terms.

What makes us happy
is different now.

New traditions
and things to explain.

Time slowed down a bit
for the world to see
the bow after the rain.

We need a little more sunshine, more compassion, patience and grace.

Rosie Ann thought, *Little things we do will spread happiness at a fast pace.*

Remember,
when storms bring in
the dark clouds,
there's a bow after the rain.

ISBN: 978-1-7364711-0-4 (hardcover)
978-1-7364711-1-1 (paperback)
978-1-7364711-2-8 (ebook)

Creative Director: Joanne Boufis
Creative Team: Paige DeBoer
and Sarah Christoff
Illustrations by: Sarah Christoff

Published by
JoFactor Entertainment, LLC
www.JoFactor.com

About the Author

The Bow After the Rain is the first book written by Kimberly Martyn DeMeo. As a member of the Society of Children's Book Writers and Illustrators, Kim loves to laugh, entertain, travel, and write. She shares her

Chicagoland home with her husband, three boys, and all of the guests that are welcome through their open doors. Her mission is to share her optimistic spirit through storytelling.

Fun Fact About the Book: Kim's house burned down during the publishing process of *The Bow After The Rain*. Miraculously, the only thing left untouched by the fire was this manuscript.

Made in the USA
Monee, IL
29 January 2022

90233724R00021